THE SINGER NOT THE SONG

adapted by Liz Driscoll

HEINEMANN NEW WAVE READERS

It was Saturday afternoon at Tony's house. Tony, Rob and Cindy were working on some new songs. They were all members of Tony's band, Trio. Suddenly, the phone rang.

So Tony went over to Brock's office to sign the contract. When Tony left, Cindy and Rob started working again. Cindy picked up her guitar. Why was she so nervous when she was alone with Rob? Tony was so enthusiastic about everything. She didn't feel nervous with him. She liked Rob too. But why was he always so serious? Why did Rob make her feel nervous?

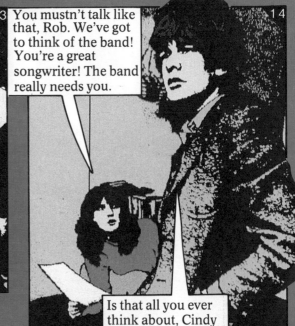

Cindy, Tony and Rob practised all day Sunday and until eleven o'clock on Monday evening. On Tuesday night they met at Cindy's flat. Tony's sister, Lucy, came too.

20 That's better, Cindy! What do you think?

Well, the new song's not perfect. Why don't we listen to it?

What do you think, Rob?

I'm not very happy with it. We need more time.

21 The first half's fine, but then I think Cindy should try and . . .

Come on, Rob! Stop worrying!

22 Poor Rob! He's worked so hard and he's still not happy. He looks so tired.

He's really worried about making the record. He doesn't think we'll be ready in time.

23 No, he's unhappy because of you, Cindy.

That's not true, Lucy.

What are they saying? I know they're talking about me! What's Cindy saying? Oh, why can't she love me?

It was nearly ten o'clock. Cindy was tired after singing for four hours. She was hungry. She wanted a break.

Okay, everybody, let's have something to eat! I'm really hungry.

That's a good idea. What about some Chinese food? There's a Chinese takeaway down the road.

24

Rob can go and get some food. Then Tony and I can listen to the tape.

25

Why is Cindy so nasty to Rob? He's so nice.

But I want to listen to it too . . . oh, all right, Cindy.

26

Poor Rob! Why should he go? You're awful to Rob, Cindy! I'm going to go with him.

So Lucy went with Rob to the Chinese takeaway. Tony put on the headphones and started listening to the tape.

Hey, listen to this, Cindy! It's the new song. It sounds great!

27

Then Cindy put on the headphones.
She sat down and switched on the tape.

After all these years we've been together . . . all these seasons we've seen together . . .

Now I can't live without your love . . .

Is that really my voice? Tony's right! The song sounds great! I can't believe it's me!

28

These words are beautiful. And they do have a special meaning. Rob loves me and he's telling the whole world about it.

29

30

And I didn't listen to him. Perhaps I was wrong. Have I made a mistake?

Suddenly, Lucy came into the room and whispered something to Tony.

31

Lucy's back. Where's Rob? What's she telling Tony? They look worried. What's happened?

32

I can't believe it! What are you saying?

Rob didn't look . . . he just stepped into the road and the car hit him! It happened so quickly, Tony. One minute he was fine and the next minute he was lying on the ground!

33

What is it? What's the matter?

It's Rob. He's had an accident. He's dead, Cindy!

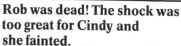

Rob was dead! The shock was too great for Cindy and she fainted.

34

Poor Cindy!

She looks awful. Will she be all right?

35

Rob was in love with Cindy, you see. He wrote his latest song for her. But Cindy wasn't interested in him. Well, that's what she said . . . and now it's too late!

So, that's why Rob was so worried. I love Cindy too, but I can never tell her now.

But Cindy didn't stop crying. Her friends didn't know what to do. Lucy made her a cup of tea but Cindy didn't want to drink it. She wanted to be alone.

40

Come on, Tony. It's very late. Let's go home. Cindy wants to be alone now. Let's go!

I'll have to phone Brock in the morning and tell him about Rob. We can't go to the recording studio on Thursday, now.

Why was I so horrible to Rob? Why was I so awful? He wrote that last song for me. I never want to sing it again! Oh, Rob!

Time passed but Cindy still felt bad about Rob's death. She didn't want to see Tony or Lucy. She wanted time to think.

41

Rob died two months ago . . . but I still feel awful. It was all my fault! Why didn't I listen to him? He loved me and I didn't give him a chance.

I don't want to sing with the band again. It's not the same without Rob.

This is the only photo I've got of him . . .

He tried to tell me what he felt through his songs.

Why didn't I listen to him? I was really stupid!

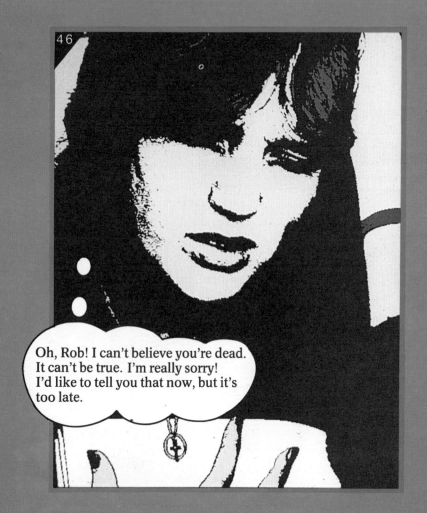

Two days later Cindy's doorbell rang. She opened the door. Lucy was standing there.

Lucy! What do you want?

47

48

Can I come in, Cindy? I want to talk to you.

But I don't want to talk to you. I don't want to talk to anyone!

Cindy, this is ridiculous! You can't stay at home all the time.

50

Rob's death was a terrible shock, I know. It was a terrible shock for all of us. But you've got to start living again!

49

Just leave me alone, Lucy!

Why do you always think about yourself? What about the band? Tony needs you! He wants to start again and he needs your help!

Never! I don't want to sing again . . . not without Rob.

You've got to help Tony. He really needs you.

51

Please, Cindy. Say you'll help Tony.

Lucy, I . . . I can't. Please don't ask me. I don't want to think about the band.

52

53

Tony's got an appointment with Brock next week. Brock still wants to make a record with the two of you. Why don't you speak to Tony? Please, Cindy.

I can't, Lucy. I never want to sing again. I never want to see Tony again!

54

You're so selfish, Cindy! You never think about other people. Poor Tony! He's nothing without you!

The next day, Cindy put on the headphones. She listened to Rob's last song . . . the song he wrote for her. She looked at the photo of Trio.

55

Perhaps Lucy's right. I am selfish. I hurt Rob . . . and now I'm doing the same thing to Tony. I'm hurting him too. Tony needs me. So I'll meet him and talk to him.

Cindy phoned Tony and agreed to meet him the next day.

56

We can start the band again . . . just the two of us. We can change our name to Duo. We've already got some great songs, haven't we?

57

The record company still want us to make a record. I've got an appointment with Brock next week.

Yes I know, Tony. Lucy told me.

Yes . . . Rob's last song was really beautiful.

58

I'm sorry, Tony. But I can't sing Rob's songs now. His songs have a special meaning for me.

I can't sing without Rob. Can't you understand that?

59

On the way back to her flat, Cindy tried to explain.

Don't cry, Cindy. I understand. Rob's songs were special to you. I know that. I'll find another person for the band.

I'd like to help Tony, but what can I do?

Rob's last song was a message for me. It was a beautiful song, a love song. I don't want to sing it again because he can't hear it.

I see . . .

Well, goodnight, Tony. It was nice to see you again. I'm sorry about the band. I hope you understand.

Cindy liked Tony. In some ways he was like a brother to her. But this kiss was something more!

What about a kiss for good luck, Cindy?

Then Cindy remembered Rob. Why was she kissing Tony? What was she doing?
No! Tony, stop it! I can't!
But Cindy . . . ? What's the matter?
64

Quickly Cindy opened the door and rushed into her flat.
65 She started to cry.

Oh no! I can't get involved with Tony! Not after Rob's death.

66

Oh Rob! I hurt you so much. I'll never forget your last song.

The words are beautiful, Rob. It's your best song.

67

It's not difficult to write love songs. I just think of you.

68

I close my eyes and think of you!

Cindy picked up her guitar and started to sing.

77

I can't live without your love.

It's a beautiful song . . . why didn't Rob write it for me? But only Cindy can sing it.

78

Cindy doesn't want to sing again. That's what she said. Perhaps she'll change her mind and help Tony now!

Cindy didn't change her mind, but on Friday night she thought about Tony's first concert.

79

80

Is Tony's concert tonight or tomorrow night?

It's tonight. It starts at nine o'clock. Poor Tony. He'll be so nervous.

So Cindy decided to go along to the Roxy and watch Tony.

81

I'll go and watch him . . . he'll never know! I'll stand at the side. He won't see me.

When she got to the Roxy, Brock was there.

Don't go in there, Cindy. Tony's terrible tonight. What's the matter with him?

What are you talking about?

82

Lucy saw Cindy with Brock and came over to join them.

He wants to make a record! I don't believe it! I'm going home.

Why was I so selfish? Why didn't I help him?

83

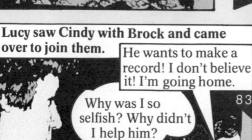

Listen to him! Poor Tony! He needs your help, Cindy!

84

To finish, I'd like to sing a love son A good friend of mine wrote it for a girl. We both loved her . . .

86

Cindy remembered Rob's words.

87

I close my eyes and think of you!

I can't live without your love.

What's Tony saying? I don't want to hear Rob's song! Oh Tony!

88

But Rob was dead . . . and Tony needed her now.

Hey, come back! Where are you going?

I know what's important. It's the singer not the song.

Cindy! I . . .

89

Don't stop singing, Tony! This is a beautiful song. Let's sing it together!

So Cindy sang with Tony. The words were beautiful . . . Cindy's voice was lovely . . . and Tony was really happy. Everyone could see – and hear – the difference.

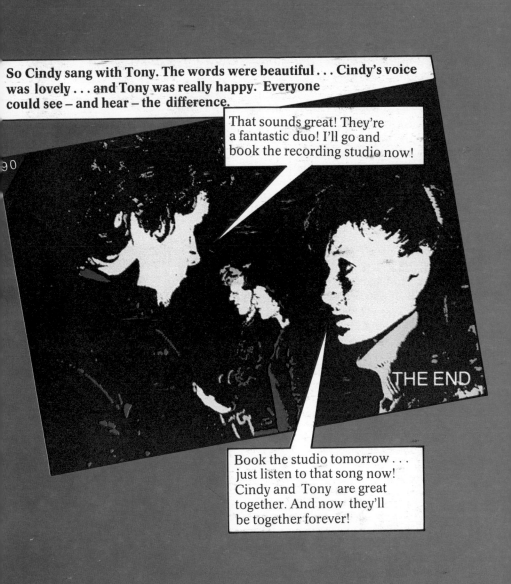

That sounds great! They're a fantastic duo! I'll go and book the recording studio now!

THE END

Book the studio tomorrow . . . just listen to that song now! Cindy and Tony are great together. And now they'll be together forever!

STORY POINTS